# Josiah
## The Boy Who Would Be King

# A Children's Bible Story and Coloring Book

### Written by DougAnDrew
### Illustrated by Miriam Rue

Illustrator: Miriam Rue (Waterslide Illustrations, Ukraine)
Text Design: Rick Quatro (Carmen Publishing Inc., Hilton, NY)
Cover Design: Tom Rood (Intelligent Design, Hamburg, NY)

ISBN 978-1-942452-07-2

For more information, contact:

McCowen Mills Publishers
Dr. Doug Stauffer, President
5709 North Broadway Street
Knoxville, TN 37918
866-344-1611 (toll free)
Website: www.BibleDoug.com
Email: Doug@BibleDoug.com

LTB Publications
Dr. Andrew Ray, Pastor
5709 North Broadway Street
Knoxville, TN 37918
(865) 688-0780
Website: www.LearntheBible.org
Email: pastorray@LearntheBible.org

# Recommendations

"*Josiah, The Boy Who Would Be King*, is an excellent book because it gleans many life lessons from a little-known but very relevant Bible character. Through reading this interesting and enjoyable book with its vivid illustrations, a young person can learn that God has a good and definite plan for each life and that one person can make a difference in his generation. It's encouraging to read of Josiah, a boy whose obedience to God helped turn a nation around. I wholeheartedly recommend this book and pray that God will use its truths to help young people learn to discern God's special purpose for their lives."

Joan Deneve is a devoted wife, mother and grandmother who has been a Christian schoolteacher for 36 years. She is presently writing her third novel in the Redeemed Side of Broken Series. Her first two highly acclaimed books were entitled, *Saving Eric* and *Freeing Elle*.

"As Christian parents, we all desire to instill eternal focus and godly purpose into the hearts and lives of our children from a tender age. *Josiah: The Boy Who Would Be King* does such a wonderful job of accomplishing this very goal by sharing the inspiring Old Testament story of young Josiah in a relatable and easy-to-understand manner. The illustrations are beautiful and will captivate young eyes and transport them to Judah as they see firsthand that God has a great purpose and divine plan for their life. As a mother, I love that this retelling of the historical account from God's word simultaneously demonstrates to my children both the Lord's limitless redemptive power and their tremendous potential for Kingdom purposes even while young."

Michelle Haynes is a small animal veterinarian and Christian mother of three. After graduating from a Christian school, she pursued her undergraduate studies and then earned her veterinary degree from Auburn University. As a life-long avid reader and collector of books, and now as a mother, Michelle is dedicated to selecting volumes that will instill in her children a love for reading and also provide for them Christian examples and stories worthy of emulation.

# Cast of Characters

 **Manasseh** — Grandfather of Josiah. Manasseh ruled Judah until his death. He was a wicked king most of his life, but ruled righteously in his later years.

 **Amon** — Manasseh's son and Josiah's father. Amon ruled wickedly for two years until his death.

   **Josiah** — The "Boy King" who became king of Judah at age eight after his father Amon died. Josiah ruled righteously.

 **Jeremiah** — A prophet of God who ministered during the reign of King Josiah.

 **Zephaniah** — A prophet of God who ministered during the reign of King Josiah.

Can you help Hilkiah, the high priest, find the word of God in the temple? Be sure to avoid the five idols.

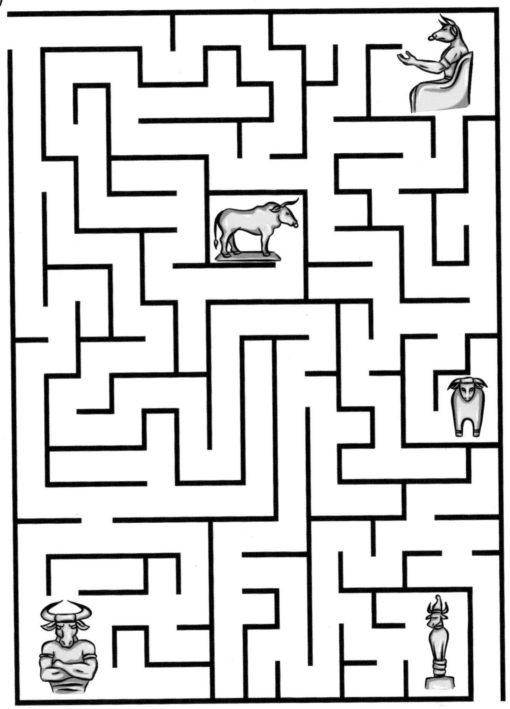

Read the story of Josiah to see what happens when the word of God is found and read to the king.

# A Prophet Foretold of Josiah

Do you think any person 300 years ago knew you would one day be born? No? Yet this really did happen for a little boy named Josiah who lived long ago. About 300 years before Josiah was born and became the king of Judah, a man of God prophesied of Josiah's life, even telling what kind of king Josiah would be.

A prophet warned king Jeroboam as he burned incense upon an altar at Bethel. The prophet told of things concerning king Josiah yet 300 years into the future (1 Kings 13:1–2).

# Josiah's Grandfather Was a Bad Man

Years before Josiah was born, the kingdom of Judah was ruled by an evil king named Manasseh. Manasseh worshipped false gods and killed innocent men, women, boys and girls. He was so bad that God promised judgment would come upon the kingdom. When people heard the news of this coming judgment, their ears tingled from fright. Unfortunately, Manasseh's evil ways caused great trouble for his son and grandson—Amon and Josiah.

Before king Manasseh turned his heart to God, he worshipped before pagan altars (2 Kings 21:1–18; 2 Chronicles 33:1–10).

# Josiah's Grandfather Turned to the Lord

At some point in Manasseh's reign, his heart was turned toward the Lord. The Bible says: "And when he was in affliction, he sought the Lord his God, and humbled himself greatly before the God of his fathers..." For the rest of his life and rule, he faithfully served God and did what was right. He worshipped the Lord and became a much better king. This change in Manasseh's life took place before Josiah was born; therefore, Josiah would have only known his grandfather during the years he faithfully served the Lord. Sadly, Manasseh died when Josiah was about six years old.

At king Manasseh's funeral, men carried his body as his son Amon and his grandson Josiah looked on (2 Chronicles 33:11–20).

# Josiah's Father Was an Evil Man

When Josiah's grandfather (Manasseh) died, Josiah's dad (Amon) became king. Amon was a really bad king. Instead of learning from Manasseh's good example in his last days, Amon chose to follow the bad behavior of his father's earlier years.  Amon was so bad that his own servants thought of a plan to kill him. Fortunately, Amon only served as the king of Judah for two short years.

King Amon's wickedness caused men to plot against him and brought shame and shock to his young son Josiah (2 Kings 21:19–26; 2 Chronicles 33:21–25).

# Josiah Had to Choose Who to Serve

During Josiah's early years, he must have been really confused. He saw his grandfather love and serve the Lord. Yet, he also saw his father do some really mean and terrible things. He surely remembered hearing his grandfather tell stories about how God had changed his life and made him a better and kind man. Yet, he also listened as his dad said horrible things about God. This must have been very confusing and sad, too, since both his grandfather and father died before Josiah celebrated his ninth birthday.

As a young king, Josiah remembered how his grandfather worshipped God and his father worshipped pagan gods.

# Josiah Grew Up Fast

Josiah was just a young boy. He should have been living out the joys of being a child. He should have been playing with his friends and enjoying the beauties of a caring and loving home. However, he was most likely deprived of most of these simple pleasures. There were certainly nights when Josiah found himself alone and cried himself to sleep. Surely, young Josiah wondered from time to time why all the other children had both grandfathers and dads and he had neither. Josiah lacked many important relationships; however, he did have what mattered most. In spite of his losses, he still had the God of his grandfather, the God of Judah, the God of the Bible.

At times, because Josiah was king, he missed out on the games played by children his age.

## Josiah Knew His Purpose in Life

With all the loss of loved ones and sacrifice of childhood, Josiah must have looked for purpose in life. He was just a boy. What could he possibly do? He could be king!

King Josiah felt very lonely as he remembered his family.

# Josiah Had Wise Helpers

Although little is known about the early days of Josiah's reign, the rest of his life shows that even as a child he must have been a good and wise king. Although Josiah was king, he likely had some godly people help him while he was still young, in much the same way that good Christian parents help their children today.

King Josiah was young but listened intently as godly men advised him in the ways of God.

# Josiah Chose to Serve the True God

As Josiah grew older, he had to make his own decisions. Would he choose to be mean and ungodly like his father's example? Or would he serve the God that changed his grandfather's life?

Young king Josiah remembered the bad and the good examples from his father and grandfather.

# Josiah Wholly Followed the Lord

Even with all the difficulties and challenges Josiah experienced as a child, he chose to serve the Lord. When Josiah was sixteen years old, he personally sought the Lord. However, Josiah was not the only one seeking the Lord at this time. When Josiah was nineteen years old, the Lord also began to speak to a young prophet named Jeremiah. These two young men, along with another prophet named Zephaniah, would be the last hope for the kingdom of Judah. Truly, Josiah was doing God's work.

King Josiah was not alone in his worship of God. The prophets Jeremiah and Zephaniah also loved and worshipped God (Jeremiah 1:1–2; Zephaniah 1:1).

# Josiah Rids the Land of Idols

As Josiah learned more about how to please the Lord, he would do the Lord's work of making Judah a better place. As a result of his godly example, people loved and served the Lord.

King Josiah led the people to destroy the wicked idols in the land (2 Chronicles 34:4–7).

# Josiah Heard of Judgment to Come

At age twenty-six, Josiah had quite the scare. He directed the people to clean up and repair God's house, the temple. As the workers were doing so, they found a copy of God's word. What a wonderful treasure! However, as God's words were read, Josiah heard of God's decree to judge his kingdom (Judah) for all the bad things that they had done in the past. This news made Josiah very afraid!

King Josiah trembled as he heard the words of God read to him
(2 Kings 22:3–11; 2 Chronicles 34:8–19).

# Josiah's Response Pleased the Lord

Josiah feared the Lord and loved Him, too. The last thing Josiah wanted to do was upset the Lord. When he heard that judgment was coming, Josiah wanted to know what God wanted him to do as king. This pleased God! In fact, God was so pleased with Josiah's tender heart that God promised to wait until Josiah died before He would bring judgment upon the kingdom.

King Josiah sent men to seek the Lord's will for the kingdom of Israel (2 Kings 22:12–20; 2 Chronicles 34:20–28).

# Josiah Led His People to Serve the Lord

Josiah must have been greatly relieved to hear the news that God was pleased with him. Yet, he went right to work telling the people in his kingdom that judgment was soon coming from the Lord. He told the people that they needed to live for the Lord and to please Him in all that they did. He cleaned the house of God and removed from the kingdom everything that displeased the Lord in any way.

King Josiah destroyed the idols in the kingdom and stopped the priests from their evil ways (2 Kings 23:1–15; 2 Chronicles 34:29–33).

# Josiah Cleansed the Land

As Josiah was doing God's work, he noticed a cemetery where evil priests had been buried. Three hundred years earlier, God's prophet had already prophesied what Josiah was about to do in that cemetery. Josiah had the bones of these evil men dug up and burned to demonstrate God's displeasure with their evil ways. After this, Josiah saw another cemetery marker and asked who was buried there. The men told him that it was the burial place of the man of God who had prophesied of Josiah so many years earlier. In order to honour the man of God, Josiah told the men to leave that burial place alone.

King Josiah rid the land of bad examples and praised the good (compare 2 Kings 23:16 with 1 Kings 13:1–2; 2 Kings 23:17–18).

# Josiah Celebrated the Passover

As soon as Josiah finished his mission, he commanded the people to keep a feast to the Lord and to worship the Lord according to God's law. Never before had there been such a wonderful feast as this one held by Josiah. Truly Josiah loved the Lord unlike any that had ever lived before him.

King Josiah kept the Passover feast with his faithful people
(2 Kings 23:19–25; 2 Chronicles 35:1–19).

# Josiah Died in Battle

As everything seemed to be going well for the beloved king, Josiah unwisely started a war with Egypt. During the battle, an archer shot an arrow and wounded King Josiah. Josiah's men brought him back to Jerusalem, the capital of his kingdom. That is where Josiah died. His death greatly saddened his people. He was much loved! In fact, the prophet Jeremiah proclaimed a lamentation (an expression of great sadness) about the life of Josiah, and many singers sang songs of his greatness. Josiah faithfully served as king of Judah for thirty-one years.

The people mourned at the death of king Josiah (2 Kings 23:29–30; 2 Chronicles 35:20–27).

# Israel Remembered Its Kings

The troubles that harmed the kingdom of Judah were brought about by the bad example and ungodly leadership of king Manasseh, Josiah's grandfather. Yet, the change God made in Manasseh's life also ultimately spared Josiah from experiencing those same troubles. If you know a changed person with a bad past, consider Manasseh's changed life as an example of the blessings that can follow. Never think that others are unworthy of God's love or beyond God's power to change for His glory. God is surely the God of second chances.

The people of the kingdom remembered well the lives of the kings of the past (2 Kings 23:26–27).

# What Will You Do?

Josiah faithfully served God as the king of Judah. While God most likely will never call you to be a king like Josiah, He has something in mind for each and every person to do for Him. You may ask, "What can I do for Him?" You may think, "I am only a child." If God can use an eight-year-old boy to sit upon the throne of a kingdom, surely He can use you today! Josiah made the choice to serve the God Who had changed his grandfather, and that choice changed a nation. Maybe God wants to use you in a mighty way, too. Will you be the next Josiah for this generation?

The End

Even today, families can learn how to live godly lives from the example of king Josiah.

# Can You Find the Words?

```
J   E   A   M   O   G   J   H   H

S   I   B   A   M   O   N   A   A

C   G   L   N   I   J   W   I   V

R   H   O   A   O   G   O   M   K

O   T   D   S   B   T   R   E   Z

L   B   I   S   D   A   C   R   E

L   A   B   E   O   M   O   E   M

H   C   S   H   A   D   U   J   O

Z   E   P   H   A   N   I   A   H
```

1. AMON
2. MANASSEH
3. ZEPHANIAH
4. JOSIAH
5. SCROLL
6. JEREMIAH
7. JUDAH
8. CROWN
9. KING
10. IDOL
11. EIGHT

# God's Invitation to You

Josiah's faith in God's word made him a great child and a great king. You too can be great! How? By believing and acting upon God's offer of salvation! Whether it is telling lies, disobeying parents, or being mean to others—the Bible says that all of us have sinned.

> **Romans 3:23** *For all have sinned, and come short of the glory of God;*

Because of our sin, none of us is good enough to get to heaven. We all do bad things, and those bad things have eternal consequences. However, the Bible also says that Christ died for us even though we were sinners.

> **Romans 5:8** *But God commendeth his love toward us, in that, while we were yet sinners, Christ died for us.*

When Christ died on the cross, He died to take the punishment for all the bad things we have done or ever will do. Because Jesus was not just a man but also God, He did not stay dead, but rose again on the third day. In order to receive His forgiveness and salvation, we must feel bad for our sin, and acknowledge our wrongdoing by asking God to forgive us and save us. The Bible promises:

> **Romans 10:13** *For whosoever shall call upon the name of the Lord shall be saved.*

Why not believe the Bible and ask God to save you right now? By trusting in Christ's sacrifice of Himself we can have forgiveness of sins through His blood.

> **Colossians 1:14** *In whom we have redemption through his blood, even the forgiveness of sins:*

Ask God for wisdom and the truth to open up your heart.

A prophet warned king Jeroboam as he burned incense upon an altar at Bethel. The prophet told of things concerning king Josiah yet 300 years into the future (1 Kings 13:1–2).

Before king Manasseh turned his heart to God, he worshipped before pagan altars **(2 Kings 21:1-18; 2 Chronicles 33:1-10).**

At king Manasseh's funeral, men carried his body as his son Amon and his grandson Josiah looked on (2 Chronicles 33:11–20).

King Amon's wickedness caused men to plot against him and brought shame and shock to his young son Josiah (**2 Kings 21:19–26; 2 Chronicles 33:21–25**).

As a young king, Josiah remembered how his grandfather worshipped God and his father worshipped pagan gods.

At times, because Josiah was king, he missed
out on the games played by children his age.

King Josiah felt very lonely as he
remembered his family.

King Josiah was young but listened intently as godly men advised him in the ways of God.

Young king Josiah remembered the bad and the good
examples from his father and grandfather.

King Josiah was not alone in his worship of God.
The prophets Jeremiah and Zephaniah also loved and
worshipped God **(Jeremiah 1:1-2; Zephaniah 1:1).**

King Josiah led the people to destroy the wicked idols in the land (2 Chronicles 34:4–7).

King Josiah trembled as he heard the words of God read to him (2 Kings 22:3–11; 2 Chronicles 34:8–19).

King Josiah sent men to seek the Lord's will for the kingdom of Israel (**2 Kings** 22:12–20; **2 Chronicles** 34:20–28).

King Josiah destroyed the idols in the kingdom and stopped the priests from their evil ways **(2 Kings 23:1–15; 2 Chronicles 34:29–33).**

King Josiah rid the land of bad examples and praised the good (**compare 2 Kings 23:16 with 1 Kings 13:1–2; 2 Kings 23:17–18**).

King Josiah kept the Passover feast with his faithful people (**2 Kings 23:19–25; 2 Chronicles 35:1–19**).

The people mourned at the death of king Josiah
(2 Kings 23:29–30; 2 Chronicles 35:20–27).

The people of the kingdom remembered well the lives of the kings of the past **(2 Kings 23:26–27)**.

Even today, families can learn how to live godly lives from the example of king Josiah.